23 April 1988

To Jamie,
With our love on your
First Reconciliation Day.
Mom & Dad

# GROWING UP
## with My Family

**GROWING UP WITH GOD SERIES** ®

## V. GILBERT BEERS
### Illustrated by HELEN ENDRES

**HARVEST HOUSE PUBLISHERS**
Eugene, Oregon 97402

**GROWING UP WITH MY FAMILY**

Copyright © 1987 by V. Gilbert Beers
Published by Harvest House Publishers
Eugene, Oregon 97402

Library of Congress Catalog Card
    Number 87-081044
ISBN 0-89081-526-7

**Printed in the United States of America.**

# BEFORE YOU READ

GROWING UP WITH MY FAMILY is part of The Muffin Family series, GROWING UP WITH GOD. Each story is really two stories—a Bible story, with a Bible truth about the way a Bible-time person lived for God, and a Muffin Family story with that same Bible truth at work in a family much like yours.

Each Bible story/Muffin story couplet emphasizes one important Bible teaching. At the heart of that Bible teaching is a moral and spiritual value—*forgiveness, patience, kindness, love, thankfulness*, and others.

The Muffin Family, a family much like the one you want your family to be, shows you how to live as God's friends should. Like the rest of us, they are not perfect, but they solve their problems the way God's friends should.

At the end of each Bible story/Muffin story couplet, you will find two pages of Muffin application, to help you and your child apply the Bible teaching and moral/spiritual value to the life of your child.

A color-coding system helps you find your way through this book. The book has three sections, "Helping My Family," "Loving My Family," and "Working For God With My Family." Each section has a different identifying color which begins on the contents page (What You Will Find in This Book) and continues through that section. Bible stories are identified with a color-coded line around the margin. Muffin Family stories have a color-coded bar at the bottom. Muffin application pages have a color-coded line around the pages. Each section title page has a large color-coded border. Labels at the bottom of the pages identify A Muffin Bible Story, A Muffin Family Story, and A Muffin Application.

The Muffin Family Growing Up With God series consists of:

**Growing Up With Jesus**
**Growing Up With My Family**
**Growing Up to Praise God**
**Growing Up With God's Friends**

# TO PARENTS AND TEACHERS

How much would you do to help your child know God? What would you give if that was the way to do it?

God has given us a simple way to know Him. Read His Word, the Bible. But the Bible is not always easy for a child to understand without help.

That's why we have created The Muffin Family books. The Muffin Family is a bridge between the people of the Bible and the children in your home and neighborhood.

Bible stories are retold in the language of today. Bible people come alive and your child will begin to feel at home in Mary's home or Jacob's tent. Your child will laugh with these people of long ago, play with them, and feel part of their families.

Bible truth comes to life for today. What little Miriam learned from God isn't that different from the lessons God has for Mini Muffin and your child.

From time to time you will see a make-believe story, a touch of fantasy. We clearly mark these places so your child will never confuse what is fact and what is fantasy. But fantasy is part of the fun of growing up.

It's time now to have fun growing up with The Muffin Family. You'll be glad you did.

# What You
# Will Find
# in This Book

# WORKING FOR GOD
# WITH MY FAMILY

# Helping My Family

# A Basket for Baby Moses

**Exodus 2:1-10**

Amram always looked tired when he came home. Each day he worked as a slave, making bricks for Pharaoh, king of Egypt.

One night Amram looked not only tired, but worried and afraid. "What is the matter?" his wife Jochebed asked.

"Haven't you heard?" Amram asked. "Pharaoh has told his soldiers to kill every Hebrew baby boy.

"No!" Jochebed said. "They can't do that to our baby." She held Baby Moses closer.

"They will unless we hide him," said Amram.

For three months Jochebed hid Baby Moses.

"Where can I hide him now?" Jochebed wondered one day.

"I know," said Baby Moses' big sister Miriam. "The king's men never go down by the river to look. We can hide him there."

Miriam helped her mother gather bulrushes and weave them into a little basket. She watched for the king's soldiers while Jochebed carried Baby Moses in the basket to the river and hid him among the plants.

Each day Jochebed and Miriam took Baby Moses to the river. Each day Miriam hid and watched him while Jochebed went home to work.

One day Miriam saw the princess, Pharaoh's daughter, coming. "She must not see our baby," Miriam thought. But the princess did see the baby.

"Look!" the princess said to her servants. "There is a basket. Bring it to me."

When the princess looked in the basket, she saw the baby. "What a beautiful baby," she said. "I will keep him for my own."

When Miriam heard that, she ran bravely to the princess. "I know of a woman who will take care of your new baby," she said.

"Good!" said the princess. "Bring her here."

Jochebed could hardly believe it when Miriam told her what had happened. No one would hurt Baby Moses now. And she could keep Baby Moses at home.

What a wonderful family Baby Moses had. He had a mother who would take care of him now without being afraid. He had a sister who had watched him when he could have been hurt. And he had a very happy father that night when he heard the good news.

Aren't you glad that Baby Moses' family were good helpers?

# The Wishing Stump

"What are you doing, Maxi?" Mini Muffin asked. "Why are you sitting on that old stump doing nothing?"

Mini was sure there must be something better for Maxi to do than this. "Why, Maxi? Hunh? Why?"

"Get lost, willya?" Maxi grumbled. "Can't you see I'm busy?"

Mini looked puzzled. That was the un-busiest way to look busy she had ever seen.

"Stop bugging me!" said Maxi. "I'll never get that bike in the window if I don't start my wishing for it today. You shouldn't bother me when I'm working at my Wishing Stump."

Mini looked across the street at the bike shop window. She knew that Maxi didn't have the money to buy that bike.

"I wish I could help him," Mini thought. "I wish I had the money to buy the bike for

Maxi." But of course she didn't.

Then Mini thought of a way to help Maxi. "Maxi, why don't you change that old stump from your Wishing Stump to your Praying Stump. Maybe God will help you get the bike if you pray for it instead of wish for it."

"Beat it, kid," Maxi growled.

But as soon as Mini left, Maxi began to think. "Maybe she's right. Maybe I should make this my Praying Stump."

Maxi had just started to work at his Praying Stump when Mr. Winkie, the owner of the bike shop came along. "Well, well," he said. "Why are you sitting on that stump when you could be riding your bike?"

"I . . . I don't have a bike," said Maxi. "I was just praying for one at my Praying Stump."

"Hmmm," said Mr. Winkie. "Why don't you make that your Pray and Do Stump? As soon as you finish praying, do something, like come to my shop and ask for a job. Then you can earn that bike in the window."

"Oh, I will, I will!" Maxi shouted.

Don't you think Maxi was glad then that Mini had helped him turn the Wishing Stump into a Praying Stump? Or was it a Pray and Do Stump?

# Growing Is . . .
# Helping Brothers and Sisters

### What the Bible Story Teaches

Brothers and sisters should love each other and do good things for each other.

### Thinking about the Bible Story

1. What was the name of Baby Moses' sister? Who was his father? Who was his mother?
2. Why was Baby Moses' family afraid?
3. How did Miriam show her love for Baby Moses?

### What the Muffin Story Teaches

Brothers and sisters please God when they show love to each other.

### Thinking about the Muffin Story

1. What was Maxi trying to do at first on his Wishing Stump?
2. What did Mini say he should do on his stump? How did this change the name of the stump?
3. How did Mini show Maxi that she loved him?

## How Can I Show Love
## to My Brother or Sister? By:

1. Playing together?
2. Arguing?
3. Smiling at my brother or sister?
4. Telling friends what my brother or sister did wrong today?

## The Bible Says

*If you love God, you should also love your brother or sister* (from 1 John 4:21).

## Prayer

Dear Jesus, thank You for my brother or sister. Show me how to love my brother or sister more. Amen.

# Please Let Me Help You

**Genesis 47:28—50:14**

Jacob had done so many good things for his family. But now he was dying. He knew it. His family knew it too. How could he help them now that he was old and sick?

But Jacob wanted to help his family this one last time. So he asked his sons and grandsons to come to see him.

Jacob gave his two grandsons, Ephraim and Manasseh a big hug. Then he kissed them. Almost any grandfather would like to do that when he says goodbye to his grandchildren.

Then Jacob asked God to do special things for his grandsons. And he asked God to help his grandsons do special things for God. That was called a blessing. Every son wanted his father to bless him before he died. Every grandson wanted his grandfather to bless him too.

Jacob had twelve sons. They were all there with him that day. They were not little boys

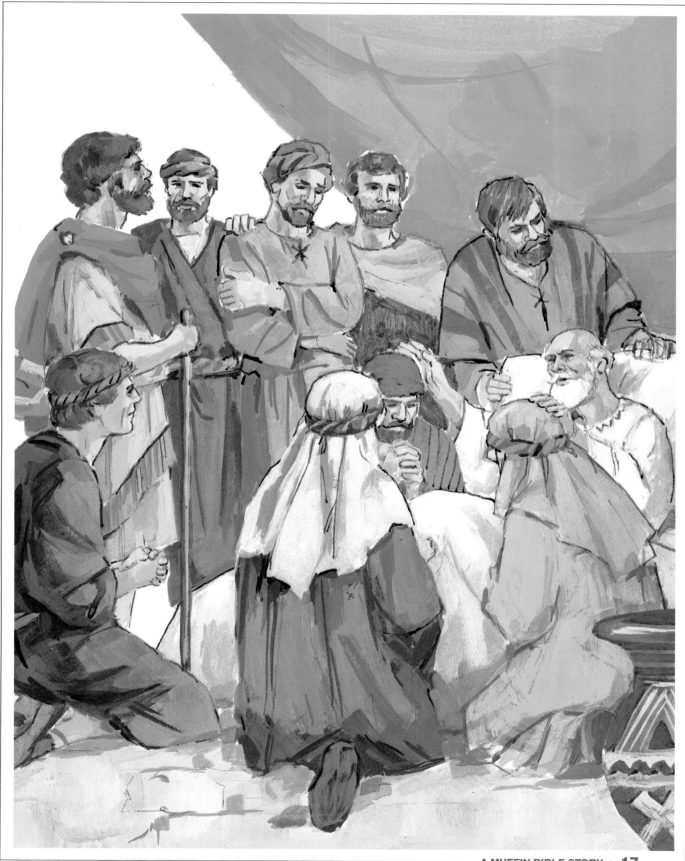

now. They were men. But Jacob was still their father and he wanted to help them. He wanted to tell them something important.

Jacob's sons came close to him as he lay on his bed. They listened carefully as Jacob told them what kind of men they were. He told them what would happen to them.

Some of the sons did not like what Jacob said about them. That's because they were not living the way God wanted. It isn't fun to hear someone tell us when we are not doing right. It certainly isn't fun to hear that from our father, is it?

Jacob was trying to help his sons be better men. Some of them had sold their brother Joseph. He had become a slave. That was a terrible thing to do. But now Joseph was the governor of Egypt. He had forgiven them for doing this to him.

But Jacob could see what would happen to these sons. He wanted to help them. There was still time for them to change. This was the last time he would talk with them. He did not want to say nice things about them that were not true. That would not help his sons. Fathers help their children most when they tell them the truth, don't they? Now it was time to tell these sons the truth, even if it hurt.

# A Help-One-Another
# Family

"Mommi."

"Yes, Mini."

"Why are so many dolls babies?"

"So you can take care of them, Mini. Little
girls like to take care of babies."

"Is that because we want to be mommis?"

"I suppose it is."

"I suppose so too. But mommis take care of other people too don't they?"

"Oh, yes, Mini. Mommis take care of big girls like you."

"And big boys like Maxi?"

"Of course, Mini. We even take care of poppis, like your poppi."

"And Poppi takes care of you too."

"He certainly does, Mini. He's a wonderful poppi. He takes good care of me. And he takes good care of you and Maxi too."

"Do you and Poppi take care of anyone else?"

"Sometimes we help Grandmommi and Grandpoppi. Sometimes we help them do things that are hard for them to do."

"Do they *ever* do special things for you?"

"Of course. They do many things for us. And they do many good things for Maxi and you."

"They're a wonderful grandmommi and grandpoppi, aren't they?"

"Yes, and they are a wonderful mommi and poppi. They are my mommi and poppi, just like Poppi and I are your mommi and poppi."

"Mommi, what's the most special thing they ever did for you?"

"Mini, they helped me ask Jesus to be my Savior. They helped me love God's Word, the Bible."

"Just like you and Poppi have helped Maxi and me do those things."

"And don't forget, Mini. Grandmommi and Grandpoppi have helped you love God and the Bible too."

"Do Minis and Maxis ever help mommis and poppis?"

"Of course, Mini. You and Maxi do many good things to help Poppi and me."

"Do we ever help you love God more?"

"Yes, we love God much more because of you. And we have learned many good things from God's Word because of you."

"Do you think Grandmommi and Grandpoppi love God more because of us?"

"Yes, Mini, they have told me so."

"Then we all help each other know God better, don't we? I'm glad we have a help-one-another-family."

# Growing Is . . .
# Helping Each Other

### What the Bible Story Teaches

We should help other members of the family by telling them the truth.

### Thinking about the Bible Story

1. Why did Jacob's sons and grandsons come to see him?
2. Did Jacob say nice things that were not true? Or truthful things that may have hurt a little?
3. If you had been Jacob would you have told truthful things that hurt?

### What the Muffin Story Teaches

Each person in your family can help the others to love God more.

### Thinking about the Muffin Story

1. How did Mommi and Poppi help Mini and Maxi love God more?
2. How do you think Maxi and Mini helped Mommi and Poppi love God more?
3. How did Grandmommi and Grandpoppi help their family love God more?

# How Can We Help Our Family Love God More?

1. Read the Bible to them.
2. Pray for them.
3. Tell them what is true.
4. Yell at them.
5. Live the way Jesus wants.

## The Bible Says

*Tell the truth in love* (from Ephesians 4:15).

## Prayer

Dear Jesus, thank You for my family. Teach me how to share Your love with each of them. Amen.

# Helping to Take Care of My Family

**Matthew 2:13-23; Luke 2:39**

You wouldn't think that anyone would want to hurt little Jesus, would you? But a wicked king called Herod wanted to kill Him. He was afraid Jesus would grow up to be king. Then he could not be king any more.

That's why King Herod wanted to kill little Jesus. The more he thought about Jesus being king, the more he wanted to kill Him.

One day King Herod called for his soldiers. "Kill Him!" he commanded them.

"But where is He?" they asked. "There are many little boys in Bethlehem. Which one is He?"

"How do I know?" Herod roared. "Kill them all!"

The soldiers ran from Herod's palace. They were afraid. They must do what he said or Herod would kill them. So they went to Bethlehem to kill all the little boys.

While this was happening, an angel talked to Joseph. "You must leave for Egypt tonight," the angel said. "You must take the boy Jesus there. Hurry! Stay there until I tell you to come home."

Joseph woke Mary. Quickly they packed the few things they had. Before long they were on their way to Egypt.

By morning they were far from Bethlehem. Mary and Joseph listened to the angel. They wanted to take good care of little Jesus.

It took many days for Mary and Joseph and Jesus to get to Egypt. "This will be our home until the angel tells us to go back to our own land," said Joseph. "We will take care of Jesus here."

Each day Mary and Joseph helped Jesus with many things. They gave Him food to

eat. They made clothes for Him to wear. They taught Him about their people back home. And they taught Him about God.

Then one night an angel talked to Joseph again. "You may take Jesus back home now," the angel said.

It was exciting to pack for the trip home. And it was even more exciting to go home again.

Joseph asked each traveler what had happened back home. But one day he was afraid. He heard that Herod's son was now the king. He was as bad as his father.

"What should we do?" Joseph wondered.

"How can we take care of Jesus in Bethlehem? This king will want to kill Him."

That night an angel talked to Joseph again. "Don't go back to Bethlehem," the angel said. "Go back to your hometown Nazareth instead. You can take care of Jesus there."

So Mary and Joseph went to Nazareth, the town where they had lived many years before. Joseph worked as a carpenter and helped Jesus learn to be a carpenter too.

Each day Mary and Joseph took special care of Jesus. That's what God wanted them to do, don't you think?

# Animal Families

Tony scooped up some feed in a pail and gave it to Maxi. "Put it in the feedbox," he said. "Then we'll get the mother pony and her baby here in the barn."

Tony's pony didn't have to be asked a second time to eat. She ran into the barn with the baby pony at her side.

"Look at her eat that feed!" said Maxi.

"And look at the baby pony," said Mini. "He's going to have his lunch too."

The baby pony came to his mother. He began to drink milk from her. The mother pony was happy to help take care of her baby.

"That's neat," said Maxi. "You take care of your pony. Then she takes care of her baby."

"Just like a people family," said Mini.

"How's that, Mini?" Tony asked.

"Well, Mommi and Poppi take care of Maxi and me," she said. "Then we take care of Ruff and Tuff. Every good dog and cat need someone to take care of them."

Maxi and Mini sat with Tony on some straw and talked about this. At last the baby finished drinking milk. Tony's pony finished eating, too.

"She's a little messy," said Mini. "Look how much she spilled on the ground."

"If we're quiet," said Tony, "we'll see another family eat."

So the three waited quietly. Before long, a mother duck came by and saw the feed. She ran toward it, quacking noisily. Five little ducklings waddled through the stable doorway and began to eat with her.

"Did you see how the mother duck helped her babies get food?" said Mini.

"Yeah, and look at them eat," said Maxi. "The pony's leftovers are the duck's lunch."

"But that's not all," said Tony. "Sit still."

When the ducks finished, the three friends sat quietly on the straw to see what would happen next. Before long a mother mouse ran from a hole under the feedbox. Then some baby mice came too.

Mini wanted to squeal with delight and talk

about those cute little mice. But Tony shushed her until the mice had finished eating. Then they went back into the hole.

"They were so DARR-ling!" Mini cooed.

"You ought to set some traps and catch those things," Maxi said. He wanted to sound important.

"MAX-II!" Mini scolded him. "Don't you say such things. Who would want to kill those darling little things?"

"Not me," said Maxi. "Maybe it would be better to catch them and put them in your bed." When Maxi said that he ran his fingers up Mini's back. Mini let out a little screech and then both of them laughed about it.

"Time to go home," said Maxi. "Thanks for showing us how your animal friends help each other."

"Now we will want to help each other more in our family!" said Mini.

# Growing Is . . .
# Taking Care of My Family

### What the Bible Story Teaches

We should take good care of our family even if we have to work hard to do it.

### Thinking about the Bible Story

1. Who told Joseph to take Jesus to Egypt? Why?
2. Why did Mary and Joseph leave Egypt and go to Nazareth?
3. How did Mary and Joseph take good care of Jesus?

### What the Muffin Story Teaches

Even animal families take care of each other, so why shouldn't we?

### Thinking about the Muffin Story

1. How many animal families ate from the grain?
2. How did each mother help take care of her children?
3. What did Mini and Maxi learn from these animal families? What did you learn?

# How Can I Take Care of My Family?

I can take care of my family by:

1. Helping Mommi clean the house.
2. Helping Poppi mow the lawn.
3. Helping Mini or Maxi set the table.
4. Throwing paper on the floor.
5. Helping Mommi wash and dry the dishes.

## The Bible Says

*If you don't take care of your family you don't live the way a Christian should* (from 1 Timothy 5:8).

## Prayer

Dear Jesus, You take good care of me, so I want to take good care of my family. You will help me do that, won't You? Amen.

# Loving My Family

# Jealous Brothers

**Genesis 37**

"Look at him!" one of Joseph's brothers complained. "Look at that fancy cloak father gave Joseph! He thinks he's better than we are."

Joseph's older brothers were angry and jealous of him. Their father Jacob liked Joseph most. He always did more for Joseph than the others. He always gave better things to Joseph, like the beautiful cloak Joseph was wearing.

One day Joseph told his brothers about a dream he had the night before. They did not

like Joseph's dream. It showed them bowing
down before Joseph.

Now Joseph was coming to see his brothers
alone in a field. Jacob was not there to take
care of Joseph.

"Let's kill him!" one of the brothers said.

"No, we must not kill our brother," Reuben
said. He was the oldest. If anything happened to Joseph, Jacob would blame him.
"Let's throw him into that dry well over
there."

So the brothers grabbed Joseph. They
tore off his beautiful cloak. Then they threw
him into the old well and sat down to eat.

Before long some traders came by. They
were going to Egypt.

"Let's sell Joseph to the traders," said Judah. "Then we will not need to kill him."

So the brothers pulled Joseph from the well. They sold him to the traders. Joseph would become a slave in Egypt.

Then the brothers killed a goat and put some blood on Joseph's cloak. They took it home to Jacob.

"Is this Joseph's cloak?" they asked. "We found it in the fields."

Jacob was heartbroken. The brothers tried to comfort him, but Jacob was too sad.

Now the brothers were sad. They had hurt Joseph. They had hurt Jacob. Now it hurt them to watch their father. The brothers were sorry, but it was too late.

# Tuff's and Taffy's Terrible Tiff

Mini's eyes sparkled as she ran into the house with a ball of fur in her arms. But Mommi's eyes did not sparkle when she saw the ball of fur.

"Mini, where did you get that cat?" Mommi asked. "And why are you bringing it here?"

"Oh, Mommi, a friend gave it to me. She can't keep it. May we? We'll call her Taffy."

"But Mini! We already have a cat. What will Tuff think?"

"She will love it!"

"Even if she does, Poppi and I won't. One cat is enough."

"Please, Mommi, may I keep it tonight?"

"Tonight only. Tomorrow we will take it to the Humane Society. OK?"

Mini took Taffy into the living room where

Tuff was sleeping. She put Taffy in front of Tuff and woke her.

"Look, Tuff! A new friend for you!"

Tuff arched her back and growled. Taffy arched her back and growled too.

"Tuff! Be nice to your friend!" Mini scolded.

Mini picked up Taffy and cuddled her in her arms. Tuff rubbed against Mini as if to say, "Cuddle me instead of that cat."

Mini put Taffy in front of Tuff again. But Tuff arched her back and growled. Taffy growled back. Then Tuff jumped at Taffy.

Taffy let out a big "YEOWWW" and took off across the room with Tuff after her. By this time Taffy was frightened. She wanted to climb something but there was nothing to climb except the living room drapes.

So she climbed them!

Tuff sat below, waiting for Taffy to let go. When she did, Taffy took long pieces of the drapes with her. Then she ran across the room again with Tuff after her.

Mommi rushed into the room just as Taffy made a flying leap across the sofa. But when she tried to jump to another chair, Taffy landed KER-PLOP in the aquarium.

"TAFFY!" Mini shouted. She fished a very wet cat from the aquarium.

By this time Taffy was so frightened that she tried to claw Mini. But Mommi rushed over with a towel to dry her. Mommi wrapped Taffy in the towel to keep her from doing anything else.

That night Taffy slept in a box that Poppi

fixed for her in the garage. Tuff slept in her basket.

After dinner, Poppi read the Bible story about Joseph and his jealous brothers. Mini thought of Tuff when Poppi asked some questions about Joseph's jealous brothers.

"Was Tuff like Joseph's jealous brothers?" Mini asked.

"In some ways," said Poppi. "Tuff didn't want you to love Taffy more than her. Joseph's brothers didn't want Jacob to love Joseph more than them."

"Was Tuff wrong? Should she be punished?" Mini asked.

"That's where Tuff is different from Joseph's brothers," said Poppi. "They knew they would hurt their family. Tuff is a cat. She didn't know that she would hurt you or Mommi. She did what any jealous cat would do."

"Poppi?"

"Yes, Mini."

"Does jealousy always hurt others?"

"Usually it does. That's because it's hard to love a person if we're jealous of him. So instead of loving that person we want to hurt him. Then others get hurt too. Sometimes even God gets hurt."

"Then Tuff and Taffy taught me something important," said Mini.

"What's that, Mini?"

"That I shouldn't be like a jealous Tuff cat or I might hurt someone I love. I might even hurt God."

Poppi smiled. "Hmmmm," he said. "Then Tuff's and Taffy's terrible tiff taught two terrific things."

# Growing Is . . .
# Not Being Jealous

### What the Bible Story Teaches
Jealousy hurts us and those around us.
Look what it did to Joseph and his brothers.

### Thinking about the Bible Story
1. Why were Joseph's brothers jealous of him?
2. What did they do because they were jealous?
3. How was Joseph hurt? How was Joseph's father hurt? How were Joseph's brothers hurt?

### What the Muffin Story Teaches
We should not be like jealous Tuff cats or we may hurt someone we love.

### Thinking about the Muffin Story
1. Why was Tuff jealous of Taffy?
2. How did Tuff's jealousy hurt Taffy? How did it hurt the Muffin Family?
3. What would you like to say to Mini Muffin about this?

# How Do I Know If I'm Jealous?

## Which of these would I say?

1. You think you are so smart!
2. I'm bigger than you are.
3. That's mine! I won't share it!
4. Let's have fun playing together.

## The Bible Says

*When you love someone, you won't get jealous or proud, but you will be patient and kind instead* (from 1 Corinthians 13:4).

## Prayer

Dear Jesus, when I get jealous remind me of Tuff and Taffy, and of Joseph and his brothers so that I won't hurt someone else and You. Amen.

# A Family that Couldn't Stay Together

**Genesis 16:1-16;
21:8-21**

"Get Hagar out of here!" Sarah screamed at her husband. "And get that son of hers out of here too!"

Abraham was hurt when he heard Sarah say this. "That son of hers" was also Abraham's son. Sarah had even claimed Ishmael as her son.

Abraham and Sarah had not been able to have a child. God had promised that they would have a son. But they grew old, too old to have a baby. Still they did not have the son God promised.

One day Sarah told her servant girl Hagar to live with Abraham and pretend she was his wife. If Hagar had a baby, Sarah would pretend that it was her baby.

But God doesn't want us to pretend those kinds of things, does He?

Hagar did have a baby boy. They named him Ishmael. Sarah pretended that he was her son, but Hagar knew that he was really her son. So Hagar and Sarah did not get along very well. Soon they began to say things that hurt each other.

Then one day Sarah had a baby boy, just as God had promised. They named him Isaac.

Now Hagar was worried. Her son Ishmael had been the one who would be head of the family when Abraham died. But now Isaac, not Ishmael, would be head of the family.

Hagar and Ishmael were hurt, and angry, and jealous. At a party one day Ishmael made fun of Isaac.

That's when Sarah told Abraham, ''Get them out of here.''

Abraham was trapped. His family was divided. He must choose between two sons.

Abraham learned too late that he could not choose one son above another. He learned too late that he had to be fair to each. When people are not fair to others in the family, everyone gets hurt.

# Play Ball!

"You heard me!" BoBo shouted at Maxi. "If you don't let me pitch, I'll take my ball and go home!"

"And you heard me too!" Pookie shouted as loud as BoBo. "If you don't let me pitch, I'll take my catcher's mitt and go home."

Maxi gulped. BoBo and Pookie were both good pitchers. And both were good friends.

"That's not fair!" Maxi complained. "You're asking me to choose between two good friends."

"We can play without one of them," Charlie advised.

"You can't play without a ball," BoBo answered snootily.

"And you can't play without a catcher's mitt," Pookie added, just as snootily.

"Looks like you two spoiled kids are saying we can't play ball," Charlie growled. "With this kind of team spirit, we'll wind up at the bottom of the city dump leagues."

"You're the captain, Maxi," said BoBo. "All you have to do is choose me as pitcher and we can get started."

"Without a catcher's mitt?" Pookie chuckled.

Maxi sat on the pitcher's mound and put his chin in his hands. What could he do?

"I'd send them to the showers," Charlie told Maxi.

"That would send the rest of us with them," said Tony. "The truth is we need BOTH the ball and the catcher's mitt. Right, Maxi?"

"Right. So we need BOTH BoBo and Pookie."

BoBo and Pookie stood like rubber statues, waiting for Maxi to choose one of them. All the other teammates watched BoBo and Pookie angrily.

"OK, let's talk some sense into these two turkeys," said Charlie. "If either of you is chosen the other will go home. Right?"

"Right!" said BoBo and Pookie together.

"So, if BoBo is chosen, he can pitch to a catcher without a mitt. Right?" said Charlie.

"Well, ah . . . uh . . ." BoBo didn't know what to say. Of course he couldn't do that.

"And if Pookie is chosen he can throw bubble gum or candy wrappers into his catcher's mitt. Right?" said Charlie.

"Well, ah . . . uh . . ." Pookie knew that he could not play ball without a ball.

"So you see, we don't have a ball game without both of you," said Charlie. "But I have a brilliant idea. Let's flip this penny. Heads, Pookie pitches. Tails, it's BoBo."

Charlie gave the penny a flip into the air. But when it landed, it rolled into a crack and stayed up on its side.

"See! Even the penny won't choose," said Maxi.

"Sure it did," said Charlie. "It says Pookie will pitch half the game and BoBo the other half."

It was such a wonderful idea that no one had thought of it. "Play ball!" said BoBo. So they did, even Pookie and BoBo.

# Growing Is . . .
# Being Fair

### What the Bible Story Teaches

Be fair to others in your family and don't put one above another.

### Thinking about the Bible Story

1. What did Sarah ask Abraham to do that wasn't fair? Should he have done it?
2. Why did Sarah want to get Hagar and Ishmael away from the family?
3. What would you like to say to Sarah? What would you like to say to Abraham?

### What the Muffin Story Teaches

Instead of choosing one friend above the other, we should do good things for both friends.

### Thinking about the Muffin Story

1. What did Pookie and BoBo want Maxi to do that wasn't fair?
2. What was Charlie's good idea?
3. How did the penny help Maxi choose what was fair?

# Is This Fair?

Maxi and Mini are playing together. Here's what they said. Which is fair?

1. Let's divide these marbles. I'll take four and you take two.
2. I get an extra turn because I'm older.
3. You put the game away while I ride my bike.
4. We'll both put the game away.

## The Bible Says

*Don't put one person above another* (from 1 Timothy 5:21).

## Prayer

Dear Jesus, You are so fair in everything. I want to be like You. Amen.

# Home Again

**Genesis 32—33**

Jacob was going home to Canaan. Twenty years before he had run away when his brother Esau wanted to kill him. Jacob had tricked his father Isaac. The old man was blind and didn't know that he was giving Jacob the blessing that belonged to his twin brother Esau.

So you see why Esau had been angry at Jacob. Now you know why Esau wanted to kill Jacob. And that's why Jacob ran away from home and went to Haran.

For twenty years Jacob had lived at Haran. He married his Uncle Laban's two daughters, Rachel and Leah, and had eleven sons and one daughter. Jacob had worked hard there and now he owned many sheep, goats, cows, donkeys, and camels. Jacob was a rich man.

But Jacob was worried. Would his brother Esau forgive him? Or would he still want to kill him?

One day Jacob decided to send some messengers to Esau. He would ask Esau to forgive him and be friends.

When the messengers came back they told Jacob that Esau was coming to meet him. He had 400 men with him. Now Jacob was even more worried. With that many men, Esau could kill his family.

Then Jacob did what we should do at a time like that. He prayed. He told the Lord how good He had been. Then he asked the Lord to protect him from Esau.

Jacob sent wonderful gifts to Esau. He sent one servant with goats. He sent another with sheep. Another went with camels and another with donkeys.

The servants were sent so that Esau would meet one every few minutes. Each servant said to Esau, "These are a gift from Jacob."

When Jacob finally saw Esau coming he must have trembled, waiting to see what Esau would do. He was almost sure that Esau would kill him and his family.

But Esau ran up to Jacob and hugged him and kissed him. Jacob had worried about something that didn't happen. But that's what we worry about most, isn't it?

For twenty years these two brothers had not seen each other. But with that one hug and kiss, Esau showed Jacob that he forgave him. Esau and Jacob had been a family divided. Now they were a family united.

# Come to Pippin's Place

A Muffin Make-believe Story

Poppi told this pretend story to Maxi and Mini about a visit they made to a wonderful island. It was a place with painted ponies and Pippins.

"Why, oh why did the Pippins say those unkind things to each other?" Mini asked. "They are just not like that."

"I know," said Maxi. "Now each has gone off in a different direction. Each thinks the others will not forgive him."

"Well, we must find them and bring them here," said Mini. "They will forgive each other as soon as they see each other."

"I know," said Maxi. "We'll get ponies at Painted Pony Stables. We can ride on them to find the Pippins."

Before long, Maxi and Mini were riding north on their painted ponies. At the end of north they found the Peppermint Pippin, sitting on a grumble log, looking sad.

"Come to Pippin's Place," said Maxi. "Your friends want to forgive you if you forgive them."

Before the Peppermint Pippin could say a word, Mini and Maxi rode south. At the end of south they found the Lollipop Pippin, sitting on a mumble log, looking sad.

"Come to Pippin's Place," said Mini. "Your friends want to forgive you if you forgive them."

Before the Lollipop Pippin could say a word, Maxi and Mini rode east. At the end of east they found the Gingerbread Pippin, sitting on a sorry log, looking sad.

"Come to Pippin's Place," said Maxi. "Your friends want to forgive you if you forgive them."

Before the Gingerbread Pippin could say a word, Mini and Maxi rode west. At the end of west they found the Gumdrop Pippin, sitting on a worry log, looking sad.

"Come to Pippin's Place," said Maxi. "Your friends want to forgive you if you forgive them."

By the time Maxi and Mini got back, what do you think they saw? Four happy Pippins, sitting together on Pippin's Place. Each forgave the other so all of them were happy. That's really the way it works, isn't it?

# Growing Is . . . Forgiving

### What the Bible Story Teaches
Forgiving helps a family forget bad things.

### Thinking about the Bible Story
1. Why was Esau angry at Jacob?
2. What did Jacob give Esau to help him feel better?
3. How did Jacob know that Esau forgave him?

### What the Muffin Story Teaches
If we've done something wrong, we must ask the other person to forgive us.

### Thinking about the Muffin Story
1. Why did the Pippins go in different directions after they said unkind things?
2. Why did they come back to Pippin's Place? What did Mini and Maxi say to each of them?
3. Do you think the Pippins forgave each other? How do you know?

## How Do We Know Someone Forgives Us?

Maxi spilled some pop on Mini's dress at school. Which of these says Mini forgave him?

1. You'll pay for my dress if it takes the rest of your life.
2. I hope Mommi spanks you.
3. That's OK. I know you didn't want to do it.
4. Just wait until Poppi hears about this.

### The Bible Says

*If your brother or sister does something to hurt you, tell him, and if he is sorry, forgive him* (from Luke 17:3).

### Prayer

Dear Jesus, I'm glad You forgave me. So I'm glad I can forgive others too. Amen.

# Bethlehem's Happy Family

**Ruth 3—4**

Each day Ruth went into the fields to work. She gathered grain for herself and Naomi. Each day Naomi thought about this wonderful girl who took care of her. What would Naomi do without Ruth? She was too old to work in the fields herself.

"Don't you think you should get married?" Naomi asked Ruth one day.

Ruth smiled and blushed. Of course she would like to get married. But to whom?

"To Boaz!" said Naomi. "He has done so much for you. He would like to marry you,

I'm sure. But he probably thinks he is too old for you."

"He's a wonderful man," Ruth whispered. "He would make such a good husband."

"Then do exactly what I tell you," said Naomi. So Ruth listened carefully to Naomi.

"Put on your best clothes," said Naomi. "Put on some perfume and go down to the threshing floor where Boaz works. When he has finished eating and lies down to sleep tonight, lie quietly at his feet until he wakes up."

So that is what Ruth did. Boaz woke up suddenly about midnight and saw someone lying at his feet.

"Who's there?" he asked.

"Ruth," she whispered.

Then Ruth told Boaz why she had come. "You are one of the closest persons in Naomi's family," she said. "According to Jewish law, you can marry me so that Naomi can have a grandchild."

"What a wonderful unselfish girl you are!" said Boaz. "May the Lord richly bless you. This is one of the kindest things you have

done for Naomi. You could marry a young man, but you're willing to marry me so that your children will be Naomi's grandchildren."

Then Boaz made a promise to Ruth. "One man is closer to Naomi's family than I am," he said. "Tomorrow I will talk with him. If he wants to marry you, then he is first. But if he doesn't, I'll take care of everything. Now go to sleep."

Early the next morning Ruth headed home. Boaz sent some barley home as a gift to Naomi.

Naomi was excited to hear what happened. "Boaz will do everything he promised," said Naomi. "Wait and see."

Sure enough, Boaz went into town the next morning to look for the other relative. When he found him, Boaz asked ten other men to hear what he would say.

"Naomi is selling all that belonged to Elimelech and her two sons," said Boaz. "Would you like to buy these things?"

"Of course," said the other man.

"If you do, you must marry Ruth," said Boaz. "That's part of the deal."

"I can't do that," said the man.

"Then I will do it," said Boaz.

So Boaz married Ruth as he had promised. As time went by, God sent a baby boy into their home. Boaz and Ruth named him Obed.

The women of Bethlehem were so happy about this new baby. They came to see Naomi. "This baby may be famous some day," they said.

The women were right! That little baby grew up and became the grandfather of the great King David.

Boaz and Ruth were thankful that God had given them a new son. And Naomi was thankful that Ruth had been so unselfish. Aren't you thankful when you see an unselfish friend?

# U or I

Sometimes Maxi and Mini could not agree. Today they could not agree on a picnic.

"Let's go to the beach," said Maxi.

"No, let's go to the park," said Mini.

"But I want to run in the sand," said Maxi.

"And I want to swing on the swings," said Mini.

Poppi winked at Mommi.

Mommi smiled at Poppi.

"I think we have alphabet problems," said Poppi.

"Alphabet problems?" asked Maxi.

"What's that?" asked Mini.

"Too much I. Not enough U," said Poppi. "Mini is thinking about what Mini wants and Maxi is thinking about what Maxi wants."

Maxi and Mini looked ashamed. They knew that Poppi was right. They had been

thinking too much about themselves.

"Perhaps it's time for the Muffin Family rag dolls that Grandmommi gave us," said Mommi.

Mommi soon came back with the Maxi and Mini rag dolls. "Who would like to do some pretending?" she asked.

"I will," said Mini. "That should be fun."

Mini took the two rag dolls and held them up for all to see. "Now, where shall we go for our picnic?" asked the real Mini.

"To the beach!" shouted the Maxi doll.

"To the park!" shouted the Mini doll.

"You always get your way," the Maxi doll complained.

"Not this time," said the Mini doll. "If you want to go to the beach, I'll go."

When the real Maxi heard that, he didn't wait for Mini to go on with her rag doll talk. "Aw, come on," he said. "You don't have to be a hero. I'll go to the park if you really want to go there."

"Quiet!" said the real Mini. "The Mini and Maxi rag dolls are still talking."

Then Mini went on talking through the rag dolls. "Aw, come on," said the Maxi doll. "You don't have to be a hero. I'll go to the park if you want to go there."

"I have a better idea," said the Mini doll. "Let's go to the park in the morning. Then we will have our picnic lunch on the beach and stay there in the afternoon!"

"That's a great idea," said the Maxi doll. "I'm glad that I thought of it."

"But I didn't," said the real Maxi. "You did."

Mini looked stern. "Will the audience please stop interrupting," she said.

"But it is a great idea," said the real Maxi. "Even if you did think of it."

"Seems that we solved our alphabet problem," said Poppi.

"And our picnic problems," said Mommi. "Now let's solve the problem of what to take for lunch."

So all the Muffins helped Mommi fix the best ever picnic lunch.

# Growing Is . . .
# Being Unselfish

### What the Bible Story Teaches
An unselfish person makes others happy.

### Thinking about the Bible Story
1. If Ruth married Boaz, an older man, their children would be Naomi's grand-children. But if she married another man who was younger, Naomi would have no grandchildren. How do you know Ruth was unselfish?
2. Why do you think Naomi loved Ruth for doing this?

### What the Muffin Story Teaches
We should be unselfish with others, for that pleases God and makes us happy too.

### Thinking about the Muffin Story
1. What kind of picnic did Maxi want?
2. What kind of picnic did Mini want?
3. How did the Muffins solve their problem? How was Maxi unselfish? How was Mini unselfish?

# Who Is Being Selfish?

Pookie and Charlie came to play with Maxi one day. Which of them is being selfish? Which is being unselfish?

1. Pookie says, "You can't play with my marbles."
2. Charlie says, "Let's play marbles together."
3. Pookie says, "We will share—three for you and three for me."
4. Charlie says, "You can play with my marbles if I'm first."

## The Bible Says

*Try to do even better than others in your giving* (from 2 Corinthians 8:7).

## Prayer

Dear Jesus, let me be like Ruth, putting others I love before myself. When I become selfish about something, remind me of the Muffin picnic. Amen.

# Working for God with My Family

# Working against God

Acts 5:1-11

All the Christians in Jerusalem said good things about Joseph of Cyprus. "What a wonderful man," some said. "What an encouragement to the rest of us," said others. They even named him Barnabas. That meant "son of encouragement."

Barnabas was a wonderful man. He sold his land and gave all his money to Peter for

God's work. That's why people said such good things about him.

Ananias and Sapphira wanted people to say good things about them too. "I know what we can do," Ananias told his wife. "We will sell our land, as Barnabas did. We will tell Peter that we are giving ALL of it for God's work. But we will keep most of it for ourselves. People will say good things about us and we will still have our money."

Sapphira thought that was a wonderful idea. She wanted to help Ananias.

As soon as they sold their land, Ananias put some of the money in a bag. Then he took it to Peter.

"Sapphira and I have sold our land," he said. "We want to give ALL the money to you for God's work."

But God had told Peter about Ananias and Sapphira. He had told Peter that they were working AGAINST Him, not FOR Him.

"Why are you doing this Ananias?" Peter asked. "Satan is causing you to lie to God. The land was yours, to keep or sell. When you sold it, the money was yours, to keep or give away. So why pretend you are giving all? You are lying to God, not to men."

No one was saying good things about Ananias now. Suddenly he was so afraid that he fell to the floor and died.

Some young men with Peter wrapped Ananias' body in strips of cloth. Then they buried him.

About three hours later Sapphira walked in. She had not heard yet what had happened. She wanted to hear all the good things that people would be saying about Ananias and her.

"Did you sell your land for this amount?" Peter asked Sapphira.

"Yes, exactly!" said Sapphira.

"Then you two have worked together to lie to God," said Peter. "The men who buried your husband will bury you."

Sapphira fell to the floor and died, just as Ananias had done. Then the young men buried her with Ananias.

The other believers were afraid when they heard what happened. But now they knew how wrong it was to work together against God, as Ananias and Sapphira had done.

No one said good things about Ananias and Sapphira. They were a family that worked together against God. How can you say good things about a family that does that?

# Pulling Together

"That's not fair!" Pookie complained. "You've got Big Bluffo on your side."

"We've also got Mini," Maxi argued. "So the three of us should equal the three of you."

"He's right," BoBo added, siding with Maxi. "If Pookie, Charlie and I can't outpull those three, we're cream puffs."

Nobody remembered who had mentioned a rope pulling contest, but someone did. Charlie hauled rope from his garage. Tony said he would be the referee. Maria decided she would make a good cheerleader.

"OK, keep it clean!" Tony urged, trying to sound important.

Charlie, Pookie and BoBo got on one end of the rope. Maxi, Mini, and Big Bluffo got on the other end. They really did make a strange looking team.

"Ready?" asked Tony.

"Ready," everyone else shouted.

"Then PULL!" shouted Tony.

There was much huffing and puffing and groaning and grunting as both sides pulled.

"Pull harder," Maxi shouted at Big Bluffo.

"I am," Big Bluffo grumbled.

"Go team go," Maria shouted. She tried to cheer equally for each side. That way, she would be sure to cheer for the winning team.

But no matter how much the two teams grunted and groaned, they seemed about equal. Neither could pull the other across the line.

"PULL HARDER, YOU BIG TURKEY!" Maxi shouted at Big Bluffo.

There are some things you shouldn't say, even when you want to. Maxi knew that as soon as he said it.

"OK, I WILL!" Big Bluffo shouted back.

As soon as he said that, Big Bluffo left Maxi's side and went over to Charlie's side.

With one mighty UNGHHH, Big Bluffo, Charlie, Pookie, and BoBo pulled Maxi and Mini into a pile of squirming rope pullers.

"We won!" Pookie shouted.

"Yeah, we're the greatest rope pullers," BoBo added.

"Go, team, go," Maria cheered. She wasn't sure if it was still OK to cheer after one side had won. But she did it anyway.

Maxi and Mini wanted to say a few things. But when it's four against two, some things are better not said. Especially if one of the four is Big Bluffo.

The big rope pulling contest was over. Maxi and Mini headed home.

Maxi was still brooding about the contest when Poppi read about Ananias and Sapphira after dinner. Then Poppi asked if anything exciting had happened that day. Maxi told about the contest and what Big Bluffo did.

"Just like Ananias and Sapphira," said Poppi.

"How?" asked Maxi.

"Everyone thought Ananias and Sapphira were pulling on God's end of the rope," said Poppi. "Suddenly they went to the other end. When they did, they really messed things up."

"I want to pull FOR God!" said Mini.

"Me too!" said Maxi.

"Then the rope pulling contest made you a winner," said Poppi. "A real winner on God's side."

# Growing Is . . .
# Helping God

### What the Bible Story Teaches

It is not enough to say we are helping God, we must really help Him.

### Thinking about the Bible Story

1. Were Ananias and Sapphira helping God by giving money to Him? Were they helping God by lying about the money they gave? Why not?
2. Does God want our help if we lie about it to make ourselves look good? Why not?

### What the Muffin Story Teaches

If you don't pull on my side you pull against me. If you don't pull on God's side you pull against Him.

### Thinking about the Muffin Story

1. Which team pulled best at first? Why?
2. What happened then? Why did one team pull much better than the other?
3. Can you do better things for God when you pull on His side? Why?

# How Can Maxi Help God?

Maxi said he wants to help God. But what should he do?

1. Maxi should read his Bible so he will know more about God.
2. Maxi should pray so he will be God's friend.
3. Maxi should sit in church all day.
4. Maxi should give some money to God each week.

## The Bible Says

*Jesus said, "If you are not for Me, you are against Me"* (from Matthew 12:30).

## Prayer

Dear Jesus, I want to help You by doing things that please You. Thank You for letting me do this. Amen.

# Working without God

**Genesis 12:10-20**

"What will we eat?" Abraham's friends and neighbors were asking.

There had been no rain for a long time. Without rain, crops did not grow. Without crops, there was no food.

"We must move to a place where there is food," Abraham told Sarah.

"But where?" Sarah asked.

"Egypt," said Abraham. "I'm sorry. We must go or we will starve."

But as they came near Egypt, Abraham began to worry. "You are beautiful," Abraham told Sarah. "Some powerful Egyptian

may want to marry you. He may kill me to get you."

"But what can we do?" Sarah asked.

Abraham should have prayed, shouldn't he? Instead of worrying, he should have talked with God. Instead of asking God what to do, Abraham decided what to do.

"I will pretend you are my sister," Abraham told her. "Then no one will want to kill me."

As soon as Abraham and Sarah came to Egypt, some men saw how beautiful she was. They ran to tell the king, who was called Pharaoh. Before long, Sarah was taken to Pharaoh. She lied, as Abraham had done. She forgot to ask God what to do.

Pharaoh put Sarah with his wives. Then he gave Abraham many special gifts—sheep, oxen, donkeys, and slaves.

But Pharaoh's people began to get sick. Somehow Pharaoh knew what was wrong. So he called Abraham before him. "You lied to me!" he shouted. "Now take your wife and get out of Egypt."

Abraham was sorry and ashamed. He knew that he had caused a lot of people to get hurt. If he had asked God what to do, this would not have happened.

Sadly Abraham and Sarah left Egypt. They went home to Canaan. But do you think they learned something that day? Do you think they would ask God to be with them next time they had to decide something?

# Truthless Todie

A Muffin Make-believe Story about Mini's Stuffed Animals

"That looks like Todie sitting by the tree," said Mini. "He looks just like my stuffed Todie on my bedroom shelf."

Mini and Maxi were walking in a make-believe land where Mini's stuffed animals lived. But here they were not stuffed animals. They were as big as Maxi and Mini.

"Are you Todie?" Mini asked.

"Truthful Todie," said Todie.

"Truthless Todie," Buffy Bear whispered.

"He almost never tells the truth."

"Careful what you say, BB," said Todie. "If you don't, I won't sell you this amazing Todemobile. It's brand new and just for you, you know."

Suddenly Todie's cap began to grow.

"What's happening?" Mini whispered to Buffy Bear.

"See! He's not telling the truth," said Buffy Bear. "That's what happens when he isn't telling the truth. His cap grows!"

"It's the ONLY way you can get around in this land," Todie said.

Todie's cap grew some more.

"But why would Buffy Bear want to buy a Todemobile?" Maxi asked. "He's not a toad."

"Neither am I," said Todie. "I'm a frog."

"I've always wanted to ask you about that," said Mini. "Why ARE you called Todie when you're not a toad?"

"And I've always wanted to ask you about your name," said Todie. "Why are you called Mini Muffin. You're not even one muffin, and certainly not many of them."

Nobody knew what to say about either name. So everyone said nothing. That's really not a bad idea when you don't know what to say.

"You must buy this Todemobile," said Todie. "It gets eighty miles per gallon."

"Gallon of what?" asked Maxi.

"Who cares?" said Todie. "As long as it gets eighty. It will run on anything." Todie's cap grew bigger and bigger.

"How much does it cost?" Mini asked.

"Five hundred down and twenty per month," said Todie. "It's in perfect condition. A little old frog drove it." Todie's cap was getting as big as he was by this time.

"Five hundred what?" asked Maxi.

"Who cares?" said Todie. "As long as you pay on time."

"Let's get out of here," said Buffy Bear. "That cap will get bigger and bigger until he tells enough truth to get it small."

"Next time I start to tell a lie, I'll remember Todie's cap!" said Mini. "Me too!" said Maxi. Will you?

# Growing Is . . .
# Telling the Truth

## What the Bible Story Teaches

When you lie about something, it's because you forgot to ask God to help you.

## Thinking about the Bible Story

1. What lie did Abraham and Sarah tell? Why did they do this?
2. If Abraham had asked God what to do, would he have lied? Why not?

## What the Muffin Story Teaches

One lie leads to another lie and before long we look silly to others.

### Thinking about the Muffin Story

1. What happened to Todie's cap when he lied?
2. Do you think we would need to tell a second lie if we never told the first? Why not?
3. Why is Jesus sad when we lie?

# Why Not Tell the Truth?

Maxi broke his neighbor's window. His neighbor asked Maxi if he did it. What would you like to say to Maxi if he said:

1. Mini did it.
2. I'm sorry, I did it. I'll be glad to work for you until it's paid for.
3. Your cat jumped through it.

## The Bible Says

*Tell each other the truth* (from Zechariah 8:16).

## Prayer

Dear Jesus, I know You would never tell a lie. Please help me to be just like You. Amen.

# Working for God

Acts 18:1-11,18,19,24-26

"Good news!" Paul said wherever he went. In each city Paul told about Jesus.

Some people laughed. Others believed. But Paul kept going from city to city. He kept telling people the Good News.

One day Paul went to Greece. He went to a big city called Athens. He had never been there before.

"What will these people say?" Paul wondered.

Paul went to the top of a hill where some city leaders met. He told the people there about Jesus. But the people would not believe.

"I will go to another city," said Paul. So he went to Corinth. But most of the people there did not believe either. Paul needed a friend.

One day he met a man named Aquila and his wife Priscilla. They made tents to sell. So did Paul. They had been chased out of a city because of what they believed. So had Paul.

"Stay at our house, and make tents with us," they told Paul. So he did. Before long they were good friends.

While they made tents together, Paul told Priscilla and Aquila about Jesus. They listened. Then they accepted Jesus as their

Savior. They began to help Paul tell others about Jesus.

Paul kept telling people in Corinth about Jesus. Before long there was a little church there. Priscilla and Aquila worked with Paul in this little church.

At last it was time for Paul to leave Corinth. "We will go with you," said Priscilla and

Aquila. They wanted to work together for God in other places.

So the three sailed to a place called Ephesus. Paul had to go on. But Priscilla and Aquila stayed there and worked together with the people who believed in Jesus.

One day a man named Apollos came to town. He was a wonderful speaker. But he did not know Jesus. So Priscilla and Aquila told Apollos about Jesus. They helped Apollos accept Jesus as his Savior.

Apollos spoke again. But this time he talked about Jesus. Then he worked with Priscilla and Aquila.

This husband and wife wanted to work for God. Paul was glad they did. And Jesus was glad they did too.

That's a good idea for our families today, isn't it?

# A Story about YOU

This is a story about YOU. Your name may be Mary or John or Joe or Kathy. But whatever it is, whenever you see ✵, say YOUR name. If there are two or more of you reading this, say all your names whenever you see ✵. So this is a story about today, when you come to Mini's and Maxi's house to play.

"Mommi! Poppi! Guess who's coming to play with us today?" Maxi and Mini shouted.

"Who?" asked Mommi.

"!" said Maxi (don't forget to say YOUR name).

"Oh, dear," said Mommi. "I hope the house is clean. What if ⁂'s mommi comes too?"

"Don't worry about that," said Poppi. "⁂'s mommi understands those things. She would probably be worried if you dropped in with Maxi or Mini."

Mommi laughed. "She shouldn't be," she said. "I'm just plain Mommi Muffin."

"Good! Now we've settled that," said Poppi. "So let's all pitch in and help plain Mommi Muffin clean up the place. She will feel better if the house is clean and neat when  comes."

Mommi ran the vacuum. Mini dusted. Maxi straightened the furniture. Poppi shook out the carpets. Before long the house was neat and clean.

"See what happens when we work together?" said Poppi. "We have fun together and get things done too."

"I was just thinking," said Mini.

"Something new?" Maxi laughed.

Mini ignored that. "But I was thinking how nice it would be if could see how we work together as a family," said Mini. "Now will see only a neat house and not how the Muffin family works together for God."

"I guess you will have to tell how we work together for God," said Poppi. "But don't forget to tell WHY we work together for God."

"Because we love each other," said Mini.

"And because we love God," said Maxi.

Maxi and Mini almost jumped when the doorbell rang. "It's !" said Maxi.

Maxi and Mini ran to the door and opened it. And there YOU are. Hope you have fun today playing with Maxi and Mini. And don't forget to notice how the Muffins work together, and play together, for God.

# Growing Is . . .
# Helping Each Other

### What the Bible Story Teaches
We help God more when we help each other do His work.

### Thinking about the Bible Story
1. How did Priscilla and Aquila help Paul do God's work?
2. How did Paul help Priscilla and Aquila do God's work?
3. Why do you think they did more for God by working together?

### What the Muffin Story Teaches
We do more work and better work when we work together. It's even more fun when we love each other and love God.

### Thinking about the Muffin Story
1. Why did the Muffins work together to clean the house? Why not tell Mommi to do it all?
2. How do you know that the Muffins love each other?
3. How do you know they love God?

# How Can We Help Each Other?

The Muffins want to go on a picnic tomorrow. But Mommi has to get dinner, fix lunch for the picnic, clean the house, and do a dozen other things. What should Poppi, Maxi, and Mini do?

1. Tell Mommi to hurry and get her work done.
2. Help Mommi get her chores done.
3. Blame Mommi for not getting to the picnic earlier.

## The Bible Says

*Let us honor God together* (from Psalm 34:3).

## Prayer

Dear Jesus, thank You for reminding me that I can do Your work better when I help others do their work better. Amen.